STICKER ACTIVITY
HORSES
& PONIES

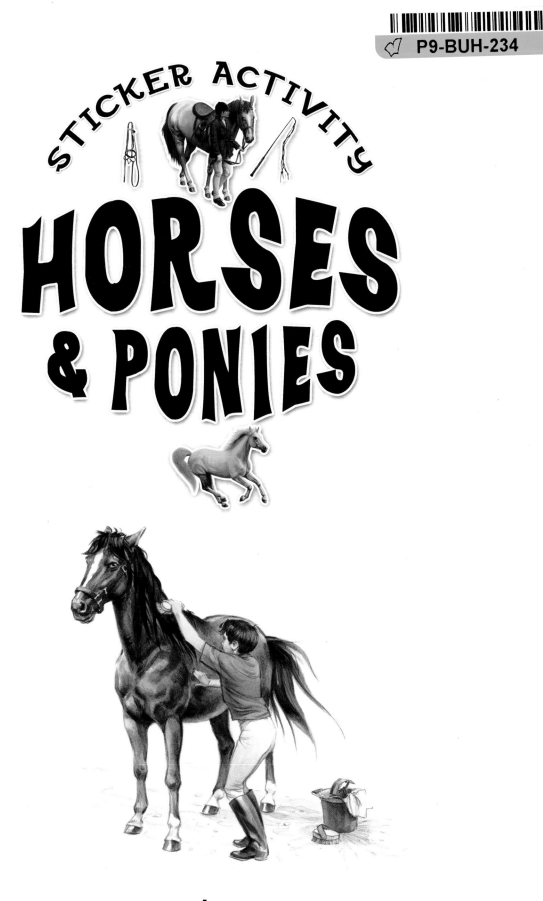

Miles Kelly

First published in 2010 by Miles Kelly Publishing Ltd
Harding's Barn, Bardfield End Green, Thaxted, Essex, CM6 3PX, Uk

2 4 6 8 10 9 7 5 3

Editorial Director Belinda Gallagher
Art Director Jo Brewer
Editor Carly Blake
Designer Michelle Foster
Cover Designer Simon Lee
Image Manager Liberty Newton
Production Manager Elizabeth Brunwin
Reprographics Stephan Davis, Jennifer Hunt, Ian Paulyn
Assets Manager Bethan Ellish
Assets Assistant Cathy Miles

ISBN 978-1-84810-260-6

Printed in China

British Library Cataloguing-in-Publication Data
A catalogue record for this book is available from the British Library

ACKNOWLEDGEMENTS
All artwork from the Miles Kelly Artwork Bank

The publishers would like to thank the following sources for the use of their photographs:
Dreamstime 15 rearing horse/Pirita; 22–23 Oldsailor
Fotolia.com 13 jockey colours/Lion beAt

All other photographs are from:
Corel, digitalSTOCK, digitalvision, iStockphoto.com, John Foxx, PhotoAlto,
PhotoDisc, PhotoEssentials, PhotoPro, Stockbyte

Every effort has been made to acknowledge the source and copyright holder of each picture.
Miles Kelly Publishing apologises for any unintentional errors or omissions.

Made with paper from a sustainable forest

www.mileskelly.net
info@mileskelly.net

www.factsforprojects.com

Self-publish your
children's book

buddingpress.co.uk

HORSES AND PONIES

Horses and ponies

For centuries, people have used horses to pull loads, plough fields and to help fight in wars.

Today, horses and ponies are ridden in many different competition events, such as showjumping and dressage.

➡ Connemara ponies are good at jumping and are often used in competitions.

Connemara pony

Here are some other horses, ponies and riders, and things they need...

Chink chink!

Making horseshoes

Charge!

Knight on horseback

Racehorse

Apple

Gallop!

Wild horses

Heave!

Horse and cart

Yee ha!

Cowboy on horseback

Giddy up!

Jockey

Carrots

Clip clop!

Horseshoe

Tap tap!

A pony getting shoed

Shire horse

Trotting horse

Cowboy

Jousting knights

Strong and sturdy

Horses and ponies have sturdy bodies. Their skeletons are strong and they have large, powerful muscles.

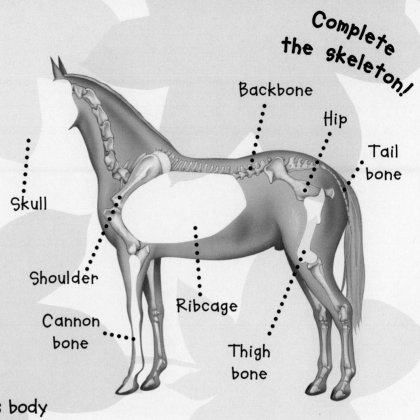

Complete the skeleton!

Backbone

Hip

Tail bone

Skull

Shoulder

Cannon bone

Ribcage

Thigh bone

Body parts

The parts of a horse's or pony's body that you can see are called the 'points'. People who work with horses and ponies have to learn what these are called.

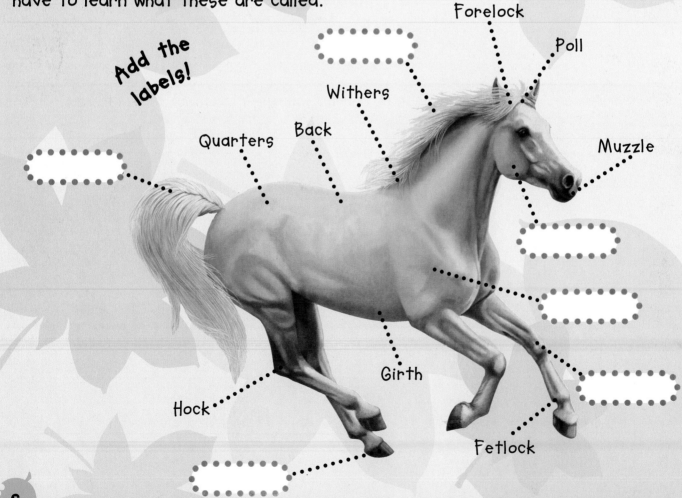

Add the labels!

Forelock

Poll

Withers

Back

Muzzle

Quarters

Girth

Hock

Fetlock

6

Hooves

Horses and ponies have a hoof on each foot. Hooves are made from the same material as fingernails.

Hoof

Bottom of hoof

Up to six months

15 years old

25 years old

Teeth

An expert can tell the age of a horse or pony by its teeth. As horses and ponies get older, their front teeth change shape from oval to round, then triangular.

Horse gallery!

Arab

Quarter horse

Przewalski's horse

Shire horses

Lipizzaner

Camargues

Find the stickers on page 12

Colours and markings

Horses and ponies have a variety of coat colours, including chestnut (red-gold), bay (red-brown) and grey (white). Some animals also have markings or patterns on their bodies.

Appaloosa horses are well known for the spotted patterns on their coats.

Appaloosa horse

Zebra

Patterns

Zebras are part of the horse family. Their fur is patterned with black and white stripes.

Colour gallery!

Chestnut

Brown

Grey

Black

Golden

DOT-TO-DOT AND COLOUR

... this piebald horse! Piebalds have patches of black and white fur on their coat.

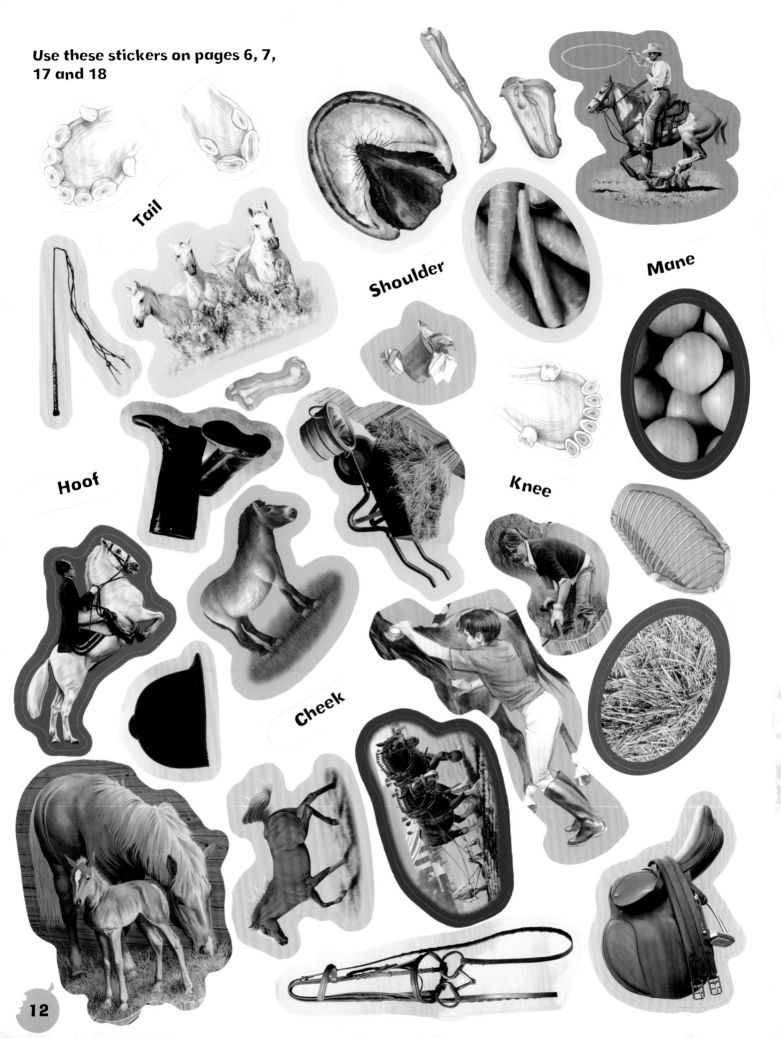

Use these stickers on pages 6, 7, 17 and 18

Tail

Shoulder

Mane

Hoof

Knee

Cheek

12

Use these stickers on pages 8, 19, 20 and 21

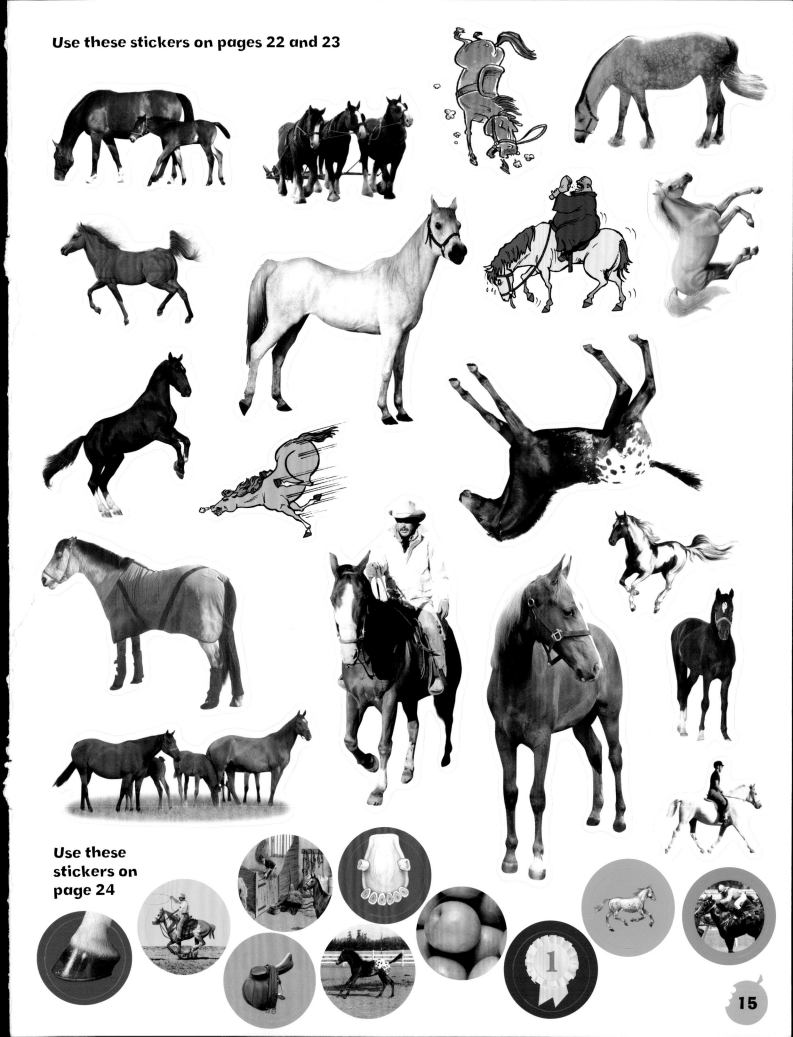

Use these stickers on pages 22 and 23

Use these stickers on page 24

15

Stable
hand

Mare with foal

A horse of
your own

**Keeping a horse or pony
takes time, money,
patience, hard work –
and lots of love and care.**

> Each morning
> a horse or pony
> should be checked
> to see that it is
> healthy.

Wheelbarrow

In the stable

Most people keep their horse or pony in a stable, which
is a warm, dry shelter. All the equipment for looking
after horses and ponies is kept in the stable, too.

Care corner

To stay fit and healthy, horses and
ponies need to be well fed and watered.
They also need to be cleaned and
groomed. Hay is the usual food,
but carrots and apples can
be given as treats.

Grooming

Complete
the picture!

Carrots

Hay

Apples

Find the stickers on page 12 **17**

In the saddle

You need special equipment to ride a horse, including a hard hat and riding boots. A horse needs a saddle with stirrups, and a bridle.

Tack is the name for the equipment a horse or pony wears, including a bridle and saddle.

Find the riding equipment!

Bridle

hat

Saddle with stirrups

Whip

Boots

18

Walk to gallop

Riders learn how to tell their horse or pony to change speed using their legs and reins.

Find the missing horses!

Walk

To walk, the rider holds the reins and squeezes with their lower legs. This pace has four beats.

Trot

The trot can be a bumpy ride. 'Rising to the trot' (standing in the stirrups for part of the trot) evens out the bumps.

Canter is faster than trot but slower than the gallop. There is a moment when all four feet are off the ground.

Canter

Gallop

For experts only! Gallop is the fastest pace.

Riding gallery!

Polo players

Jockey and racehorse

Fantasia horseman

Mounted guards

Dressage rider

It's show time!

Taking part in shows and competitions can be lots of fun. It's a great way for riders to meet new friends and bond with their horse or pony.

Add the horses to the course!

Scoreboard

Award the rosettes!

Picture puzzle

In showjumping, a rider aims to get round a set of jumps quickly, without knocking any down.

Gymkhana

At a gymkhana, riders take part in lots of different games. Young riders can test their riding skills in a variety of competitions, including the flag race.

Flag race

In a flag race, the rider has to lean over and grab a flag while their horse is moving.

What is the rider about to grab?

Racing corner

All around the world, horses are ridden in speed races. If a horse wins, its owner is rewarded with prize money. Every jockey wears their own colour scheme.

Find the missing riders!

Green, yellow and black

Blue and white

Red and white

Find the stickers on page 13 **21**

Find the stickers on page 15

Can you find...?

Clop! ...A horse's or pony's foot

The teeth of a very old horse... Smile!

Ye haa! ...A horse ridden by a cowboy

A spotty horse... Neigh!

Home sweet home! ...A home for horses and ponies

A crunchy fruit that horses and ponies love to eat... Munch!

Giddy up! ...A piece of riding equipment that goes on a horse's or pony's back

A galloping horse... Zoom!

Well done! ...The prize a winning rider would receive

Jockeys racing on racehorses... Thunder!